SHIRE NATURAL HIS

GU00375166

BUTTERCUPS

STEPHEN BLACKMORE

CONTENTS

COVER: *Creeping Buttercup (Ranunculus repens).*

Series editors: Jim Flegg and Chris Humphries.

Set in 9 point Times roman and printed in Great Britain by C. I. Thomas & Sons (Haverfordwest) Ltd, Press Buildings, Merlins Bridge, Haverfordwest, Dyfed.

Buttercups and their relatives

Buttercups are amongst the best known and most readily recognised of all British wild flowers. Whilst everyone knows a buttercup when they see one, few people are aware how many different kinds of buttercup may be found in Britain. As many as twenty-three members of the buttercup genus, *Ranunculus*, are either native in Britain or widely naturalised and several more occur occasionally as introduced weeds.

The Buttercup family, Ranunculaceae, is a large one containing about eighteen hundred members. They are widely distributed throughout all but the very coldest regions of the world and deserts, although they are most numerous in the temperate parts of the northern and southern hemispheres. There are few tropical members of the family and most of these occur in mountainous places where the local climate is similar to that of temperate regions.

Most members of the Ranunculaceae are herbaceous, or soft-stemmed, plants of comparatively small size. A few are woody-stemmed climbers. Traveller's Joy or Old Man's Beard is a familiar climbing representative of the family and is especially common in the south of England, where it is the closest approach in the British flora to the lianes of tropical forests. The Ranunculaceae includes both annual species, which complete their life cycles in a single year, and perennials, which persist for a number of years. The perennial species die back in winter, surviving through the harsh conditions of winter by means of their underground parts, which are often tuberous. The leaves of members of the Ranunculaceae are variable: they may be long and narrow, heart-shaped or divided into palmate lobes, sometimes to the extent that only the main veins remain. The flowers are generally radially symmetrical with their various parts arranged spirally around a central axis. Some members, such as Monkshood *(Aconitum*

anglicum), have bisymmetrical flowers reminiscent of a Snapdragon.

In most families of flowering plants the showy parts of the flower, the perianth segments, are of two distinct kinds, sepals and petals. The sepals are the outermost segments and are generally green; the petals are nearer to the centre of the flower and are often more brightly coloured. In the Buttercup family the distinction between sepals and petals is much less clear-cut in many cases. In some members of the family, including Christmas Rose *(Helleborus niger)* or Old Man's Beard *(Clematis vitalba)*, the greenish or white sepals take the place of the petals as the most colourful part of the flower and therefore as the part which attracts insects to the flower. Sepals usually serve more of a protective function, covering the petals whilst they are in bud and falling off when the flowers burst open. Only the true buttercups have both sepals and petals present throughout the flowering period.

The petals and sepals, which are sterile, enclose the fertile or reproductive parts of the flower. The stamens, the male parts of the flower which produce pollen grains, are numerous in the Buttercup family, whereas in many families they are fewer. The St John's worts *(Hypericum)* also have yellow-petalled flowers with numerous stamens and so look rather buttercup-like. Close inspection reveals that the stamens of a St John's wort are grouped together in bundles with their stalks, or filaments, joined together at the base. Those of the Buttercup family are always free.

The carpels are the female parts of the flower and contain ovules, each with an egg cell. The carpels of the Ranunculaceae may be free or fused together. In buttercups they are always free and each carpel contains only a single ovule. If this is fertilised it develops into a hard single-seeded fruit called an achene, which does not split open when ripe. In Marsh Marigold *(Caltha palustris)*, which looks like a large-flowered buttercup, or Christmas Rose the carpels are many-ovuled and develop into fruits called follicles which split open along their length to release the seeds. In many Ranunculaceae, for example in Delphi-

THE CLASSIFICATION OF BUTTERCUPS

FAMILY — *RANUNCULACEAE*
The Buttercup family, with 1800 species worldwide, divided between 2 subfamilies:

SUBFAMILY — *RANUNCULOIDEAE*
Carpels contain one ovule; fruit a dry achene.

HELLEBOROIDEAE
Carpels with more than one ovule; fruits follicles or berry-like.

TRIBE — *ANEMONEAE*
Leaves basal and alternate; flowers with a whorl of leaves; sepals persistent and showy; achenes not feathery.

CLEMATIDEAE
Leaves opposite, flowers without a whorl of leaves; petals absent; sepals showy; achenes with feathery plumes.

HELLEBOREAE
Flowers radially symmetrical.

DELPHINEAE
Flowers bilaterally symmetrical.

RANUNCULEAE
Leaves alternate or basal; flowers without a whorl of leaves; sepals generally falling; achenes not feathery.

GENUS — *RANUNCULUS*
The Buttercup genus: about 300 species worldwide; about 23 species in Britain, representing 3 subgenera:

SUBGENUS — *BATRACHIUM*
White-flowered aquatics, about 9 British species:
R. hederaceus R. omiophyllus
R. tripartitus R. fluitans
R. circinatus R. trichophyllus
R. aquatilis R. peltatus
R. baudotii

RANUNCULUS
13 British species in 6 sections:

FICARIA
Yellow flowers, entire leaves, 1 species:
R. ficaria

SECTION — *RANUNCULASTRUM*
1 species:
R. paludosus

EPIROTES
1 species:
R. auricomus

HECATONIA
1 species:
R. sceleratus

RANUNCULUS
3 species:
R. acris
R. repens
R. bulbosus

ECHINELLA
3 species:
R. arvensis
R. sardous
R. parviflorus

FLAMMULA
4 species:
R. lingua
R. flammula
R. reptans
R. ophioglossifolius

niums, several of these carpels are fused together in the centre of the flower. These differences have been used by botanists to divide the Ranunculaceae into two subfamilies: the Helleboroideae includes all those species with more than one ovule in each carpel, and the Ranunculoideae those in which each carpel has a single ovule.

These characteristics enable the Buttercup family to be recognised but there are a number of plants, other than St John's worts, which look sufficiently like buttercups to be confused. One of these is Herb Bennet *(Geum urbanum)*, a common wild flower of woodland margins which is often mistaken for a buttercup although it is a member of the Rose family (Rosaceae). It can be distinguished from a buttercup by its burr-like heads of fruits and by the five small sepals, or episepals, which alternate with the normal-sized sepals. The leaves of Herb Bennet are more like those of the Bramble, to which it is related. Greater Celandine *(Chelidonium majalis)* grows in similar habitats and also looks somewhat like a buttercup. The Lesser Celandine is indeed a member of the genus *Ranunculus*. Greater Celandine, however, belongs to the Poppy family (Papaveraceae), as the orange latex

3

which flows from snapped stems and the elongated capsules, which are its fruits, reveal. The Rock Rose *(Helianthemum chamaecistus)* is a wild flower of calcareous soils which is also similar to a buttercup but can be distinguished by its opposite-paired leaves and by its fused carpels, which ripen into a spherical capsule.

The Buttercup family includes few plants of economic importance although there are many well known garden plants amongst their numbers. These include Pasque Flowers *(Pulsatilla)*, Love-in-a-mist *(Nigella)*, Larkspurs *(Delphinium)*, Columbine *(Aquilegia)*, Globe Flower *(Trollius)*, Monkshood *(Aconitum)* and numerous varieties of climbing *Clematis*. A few true buttercups are grown in gardens: the Lesser Celandine *(Ranunculus ficaria)* is sometimes planted in shady corners and Greater Spearwort *(R. flammula)* makes an attractive pond-side plant. Most of the garden flowers of the Buttercup family originated in the wild in Europe and have, through long cultivation, been improved and the most colourful varieties selected.

Ranunculus, the buttercup genus, contains about three hundred species and is characterised by having true sepals and petals present. The petals have prominent nectar-containing pouches, called honey leaves, on their upper surfaces. The anthers are numerous, as are the carpels, which are spirally arranged on a domed receptacle in the centre of the flower. Important characteristics for distinguishing between the species of *Ranunculus* are the colour of the petals, the shape of the leaves, the hairiness of the various parts of the plant and details of the achenes. In Britain representatives of three subgenera are found. Two of these are quite large, one terrestrial and one aquatic, with a number of species in each, and the remaining subgenus contains only the Lesser Celandine. The subgenus which contains the yellow-flowered terrestrial buttercups can be divided into six sections, which are recognised by similar characteristics to those which distinguish the species. In this book the various sections and subgenera are described under the headings of the habitats in which they grow.

The structure and life of buttercups

The general structure of a buttercup is often described in books about plants because in many ways they provide a good example of a typical herbaceous plant, and because they are so familiar.

The underground parts of buttercups are variable: some species have a swollen tuberous base to the stem; others have runners above or below ground and some species have small fleshy tubers in amongst their roots. Swollen underground parts are associated with the storage of food reserves manufactured in the leaves, and runners with the spread and colonisation of new ground by the plant. Both contribute to the success of the buttercups as weeds: the tubers and swollen stems help them to survive the cutting back of their aerial parts, and the runners enable them to spread rapidly if unchecked. Since the underground parts of buttercups are so variable they provide a useful means of identification, especially when weedy buttercups are being eradicated. Of the three commonest buttercup species the Creeping Buttercup *(Ranunculus repens)* has horizontal runners above ground, which root and form new plants at intervals. The Bulbous Buttercup *(R. bulbosus)* has a swollen stem base, or corm, below ground, whilst the Meadow Buttercup *(R. acris)* lacks either corms or runners. A rare and very local buttercup, the Fan-leaved Buttercup *(R. paludosus)*, has both a swollen stem base and small rounded tubers amongst its roots. The Lesser Celandine has rather different elongated tubers which taper towards the ends. The several species of spearworts have extensive runners which root at the node to establish new plants. The underground parts do not always enable a precise identification to be made; if leaves, flowers or fruits are present accurate identification should be possible.

Buttercup stems also exhibit some variation. They are not always erect, or

Plate 1. *A flower of Meadow Buttercup (R. acris) cut in half, showing, from the centre outwards, unripe ovaries, anthers which are beginning to release pollen, petals with flap-like nectaries and sepals.*

upright. The runners are specialised horizontal stems which spread from the base of the plant, sometimes underground or underwater, and which produce roots and leaves at intervals. These leaves and roots develop from buds which occur at intervals along the runners and correspond to those on the upright stems. Some buttercups have stems which lie close to the ground at their bases and then gradually curve upright. This habit is seen in Meadow Buttercup, Small-flowered Buttercup (*Ranunculus parviflorus*), Greater Spearwort (*R. lingua*) and in many plants of Bulbous Buttercup. Other species, including Creeping Buttercup, fan-leaved Buttercup and Corn Crowfoot (*R. arvensis*) have erect stems which arise vertically from the top of the root system. Amongst aquatic buttercups there are species with horizontal floating stems with reduced root systems. Buttercup stems, like those of other plants, contain tissues which carry water from the ground to the aerial parts of the plant and food manufactured in the leaves to other parts, including the underground storage organs, if present. They contain relatively few of the thick-walled xylem cells which make up the woody parts of shrubs and trees. Since there are so few of these cells

present, the stems of buttercups die back in winter, when the leaves also shrivel and fall. In many species a rosette of leaves lying at ground level may persist through the winter.

Two features of buttercup stems important in the recognition of species are the presence of furrows or grooves running along the stems of some species and the degree of hairiness. Bulbous Buttercup, Corn Crowfoot and Hairy Buttercup (*Ranunculus sardous*) all have distinctly hairy stems, whereas Greater Spearwort, Lesser Spearwort (*R. flammula*) and Celery-leaved Crowfoot (*R. sceleratus*) lack hairs. Furrowed stems can be very useful for distinguishing otherwise similar species. For instance, Creeping Buttercup, which has furrowed stems, can be distinguished from Meadow Buttercup, which has cylindrical stems without furrows. Celery-leaved Crowfoot has stout, deeply furrowed stems which are hollow inside.

THE LEAVES

The variation in underground parts and stems is greatly surpassed by the diversity of the leaves of buttercups. These may be entire, with an even and continuous outline, or variously palmate-lobed or

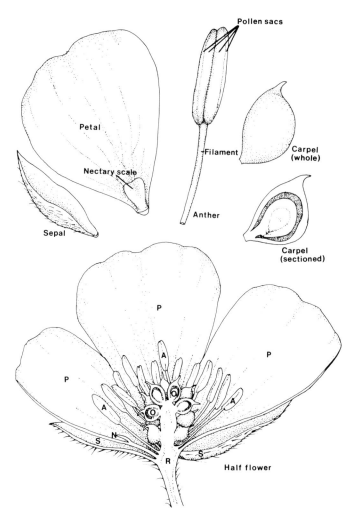

Fig. 1. *The parts of a*
buttercup flower.
A anther
N nectary scale
O ovary
P petal
R receptacle
S sepal

dissected. Entire leaves are found in the
Lesser Celandine, in which they are
heart-shaped, or cordate, in outline, and
in many of the buttercups of marshes and
water margins, such as the spearworts, in
which the leaves are ovate or lanceolate.
The three commonest buttercups all have
palmately lobed leaves which are dissected to a greater or lesser extent.
Generally the leaves highest up the stem
are the most deeply dissected. The fully
aquatic buttercups display the greatest
diversity of leaves, often having almost
entire floating leaves and quite different
finely dissected submerged leaves. Other
aquatic species have only the finely dis-

sected leaves. Such dissimilarities can be
related to the preference of the species to
slightly different habitats and may also be
modified by the habitat, as will be seen
later. Having leaves of different shapes
on an individual plant is a feature of some
aquatic plants. Perhaps the best known of
these is Arrowhead (*Sagittaria sagittifo-*
lia), which takes its name from the
uppermost leaves, which are arrow-
shaped. The lower leaves float on the
surface of the water and are more rounded, like those of a waterlily, and the
lowest leaves, which are submerged, are
narrow and strap-shaped. The floating
leaves of arrowhead are the same shape

as those of aquatic buttercups, although much larger, and these also have narrower submerged leaves which trail in the currents of water.

The type of leaf present is an indication of the subgenus or section of *Ranunculus* to which a plant belongs. Subgenus *Ficaria*, to which the Lesser Celandine belongs, and section *Flammula* of subgenus *Ranunculus* both have entire leaves. Finely dissected leaves occur only in subgenus *Batrachium*.

THE FLOWERS

Buttercup flowers are borne singly in Lesser Celandine and the white-flowered aquatic species of subgenus *Batrachium*. In other buttercups they are grouped together in inflorescences. These are usually cymose, having a flower at the end of each growing point, the flowers which open first being the highest ones. Buttercups usually have three to five sepals, which are a pale yellow colour and may be a useful aid to identification. In Hairy Buttercup, Bulbous Buttercup, Small-flowered Buttercup, Celery-leaved Crowfoot and several members of subgenus *Batrachium* the sepals are reflexed, or strongly folded backwards. Those of other species are spreading and this character is particularly useful as a means of distinguishing the very common Bulbous Buttercup from Creeping and Meadow Buttercup, with which it frequently grows.

The petals vary in colour and in number from none to ten. Yellow petals occur throughout the genus except in the aquatics of subgenus *Batrachium*. The petals of Lesser Celandine are yellow when the flowers first open but often fade to white with age. The woodland species Goldilocks (*Ranunculus auricomus*) may entirely lack petals or have very reduced and uneven-shaped petals. The yellow petals of buttercups are much brighter than those of most wild flowers and have a glossy sheen when examined closely. This is due in part to thousands of microscopic starch grains contained in the cells below the surface of the petals, which reflect back the sunlight. This serves to make the flowers stand out against a background of green vegetation and thus helps attract insects which may carry out pollination. The yellow coloration itself is due to pigments dissolved in the sap of cells in the petals. These pigments are lacking in subgenus *Batrachium*, except in the yellow blotch at the base of each petal. When the ovules of a buttercup have been fertilised and the fruits are beginning to ripen the sepals and petals are shed, usually followed by the stamens.

The stamens of buttercups are numerous. Each has a narrow yellow filament bearing the anther with its four pollen sacs. These pollen sacs split open to release the pollen grains towards the outside of the flower. The pollen is bright yellow in colour and may often be seen lying on the surface of the petals. In the centre of the flower are the carpels, each of which contains the single ovule. At the top of the carpel is the stigma, a region on which pollen grains may germinate. The surfaces of the carpels and their shape are important characters for recognising species and sections. These differences can best be seen after the ovules have been fertilised, when they begin to grow and their surface features are more apparent. A hand lens capable of magnifying eight or ten times is indispensable when looking for fine details such as the surfaces of carpels or ripe achenes.

The achenes of the three commonest buttercups are smooth with short hooked or curved beaks. The Corn Crowfoot, however, has very distinctive achenes which are much larger and have a conspicuous border running around their edges and are covered in long spines. The spines on the borders are longest and give rise to many of the common names the plant has been given. It has been called Watch Wheels and Cog Wheels from the resemblance of the achenes to the small cog wheels in the mechanism of a watch. Other names include Devil's Claws, Hellweed, Hungerweed and Starveacre, which all indicate the plant's poor reputation as a weed of arable land. Although the species was once a serious problem as a weed it has largely been eradicated by the use of purer seed stocks. As it is an annual plant it could best be controlled by cutting or clearing before the flower heads had set seed. Now that agricultural methods have been improved this species

From left: R. acris;
R. repens; R. bulbo-
sus; R. paludosus.

R. arvensis; R. sar-
dous; R. parviflorus;
R. auricomus.

R. lingua; R. flam-
mula; R. reptans;
R. ophioglossifolius;
R. sceleratus.

R. peltatus; R. heter-
ophyllus; R. heder-
aceus; R. ficaria.

Fig. 2. Achenes of buttercups: the ripe achenes of British Ranunculus species arranged according to
sections of the genus. Only three species from Subgenus Batrachium are illustrated. Drawings to the
same scale.

is much less frequently seen than in former times, a decline which has also affected other cornfield weeds including Corn Flower (*Centaurea cyanus*) and Corn Cockle (*Agrostemma githago*). Corn Crowfoot is a member of section *Echinella*, a name which refers to the small spines, or echinae, of the achenes. Two other native British species in this section are also annuals with tubercled and spiny achenes, of a smaller size. These are Hairy Buttercup and Small-flowered Buttercup.

Goldilocks has small rounded achenes covered with fine downy hairs, best observed with a hand lens. The achenes of Celery-leaved Crowfoot are small and compressed with a wrinkled surface, whilst the various spearworts have achenes with minutely pitted or indented surfaces. All members of section *Batrachium* have achenes with prominent transverse wrinkles.

THE LIFE CYCLE

The life of a buttercup begins with the germination of its seed. The seedling produces small leaves, which are often

8

Plate 2. *Greater Spearwort (R. lingua) showing flowers and the spherical heads of ripening fruits. In this species the ovaries reach maturity before the anthers shed their pollen.*

Plate 3. *Greater Spearwort (R. lingua). After fertilisation the achenes begin to ripen and the petals and sepals fall from the flowers.*

Plate 4. *A ripe head of Greater Spearwort achenes, each of which contains a single seed.*

less deeply dissected than those of the mature plant. In the narrow-leaved species of section *Flammula* the first leaves tend to be broader and more ovate than the later ones. At first the leaves are arranged in a rosette close to the ground but most species soon develop upright stems with leaves. The Lesser Celandine is an exception as its leaves are always basal and it does not produce elongated stems.

Buttercups begin to flower from early in March, in the case of Lesser Celandine, and from May to June for most species. The majority of species are in flower for a period of about two months but some continue to flower for much longer. The Meadow Buttercup, for example, will continue flowering well into October in a mild year.

Once open, the flowers attract a wide variety of insects, ranging from bees to various small flies and beetles. These insects are attracted to the flowers by their brightly coloured reflective petals and come to find pollen or nectar as food. Buttercups produce both nectar and pollen and some of the visiting insects, such as bees, take both. Others, like the beetles, feed almost entirely on pollen, feeding directly on the anthers or on pollen grains held on the petals. Some long-tongued flies visit buttercup flowers to drink nectar. In the course of feeding these insects become covered with pollen grains dusted on to them from the anthers. The microscopic pollen grains contain the male reproductive cells which can fertilise an ovule. When the insects alight on a different flower they may carry out pollination by inadvertently brushing pollen from their bodies on to the receptive stigmas at the tops of the carpels.

Most buttercups avoid self-pollination, the transfer of pollen from anthers to the stigmas of the same flower, by not releasing their pollen at the time when the ovules become ready to be fertilised. Most buttercups are protandrous, that is the male part of the flower, the stamens, matures first. The Hairy Buttercup, Goldilocks and Greater Spearwort are protogynous, and their carpels mature before the anthers are ready to release pollen. In such species the achenes are usually beginning to mature by the time the pollen grains are released. The major advantage of these differences in timing is that they increase the likelihood of cross-pollination, that is the transfer of pollen between different flowers, which results in more vigorous offspring. Despite this some species, including Corn Crowfoot, produce pollen at the same time as the carpels are receptive and so do not always avoid self-pollination.

A further complication is that many buttercups, particularly the commonest three species, often have unisexual flowers in which the anthers are sterile and do not produce fertile pollen grains or alternatively in which there are no fertile ovules. Some unusual individuals of the Meadow Buttercup have neither fertile pollen nor ovules and are thus completely sterile. This does not always mean that the plant is incapable of producing new individuals as there are also means of vegetative reproduction by the production of runners.

When fertile pollen grains reach a suitable stigma they germinate, producing a narrow pollen tube, which penetrates the stigma and carpel wall to reach the egg cell of the ovule. This is then fertilised by the male reproductive cell. The embryo thus formed grows so that by the time the achenes ripen it has two small seed leaves or cotyledons and an embryonic root and shoot. When the heads of achenes ripen and turn brown they eventually separate from the receptacle and are shaken free. The receptacle frequently elongates during this period and this can be a useful aid in identifying the species.

Most buttercups lack special adaptations to transport the seeds far from the parent plant. Those of section *Echinella* are dispersed by their hooks on the fur of animals and those of aquatic species by currents of water.

The ecology of buttercups

Ecology is the study of the interactions between a plant or animal and its environment, that is the conditions in which it lives. Most members of the Ranunculaceae prefer moist conditions for growth although a few species are tolerant of drier habitats. Bulbous Buttercup grows well in dry pastures and other well drained places, such as stabilised sand dunes. Similarly, the Fan-leaved Buttercup is found only in dry places but has an extremely restricted distribution in Britain, occurring only in Jersey, where it is at the northern extreme of its range. It is a species of much warmer regions and extends into North Africa and India. The Small-flowered Buttercup has an essentially similar distribution but extends further northwards into Wales and England.

Most buttercups require bright light in which to grow but two British species, Lesser Celandine and Goldilocks, are woodland plants, tolerant of shade and only occasionally found in the open. Most other species are found in wet places, ranging from damp, poorly drained fields, where the three commonest buttercups thrive, to marshes or open water.

The white-flowered aquatics of subgenus *Batrachium* are especially interesting because their leaves show distinct adaptations to their environments. Almost entire leaves slightly divided into palmate lobes are found only in species growing on muddy ground that is not covered by water all year round. Two species, Ivy-leaved Crowfoot (*Ranunculus hederaceus*) and *R. omiophyllus*, a water crowfoot which has no common name, have no finely dissected submerged leaves. Three-lobed Water Crowfoot (*R. tripartitus*) and *R. peltatus*, another species which lacks a common name, have palmate floating leaves and finely dissected submerged ones. So do the Common Water Crowfoot (*R. aquatilis*) and *R. baudotii* but these two also have intermediate leaves between the two extremes. A further group of species are inhabitants of faster-flowing streams and rivers and lack floating leaves, only submerged finely dissected leaves being present. *R. fluitans*, *R. circinatus* and *R. trichophyllus* are examples of this type. In practice a further complication is that some of the water crowfoots modify the extent of dissection of leaves or the proportion of the two types present in response to the location in which they are growing.

The design of the floating leaves is perfectly suited to flotation and is of a shape found in waterlilies and other plants which share the same habitat. The stalk arises from the centre of the leaf, where it is least inclined to pull the floating blade, or part of it, under water. Similarly the submerged leaves are equally well adapted and trail in currents of water without offering much resistance to the current, which might uproot the plant. Even more importantly, their fine dissection increases the surface area through which gases can diffuse in and out of the leaves. Submerged leaves exchange gases involved in photosynthesis through their surfaces rather than through the minute pores, known as stomata, which perform this function in normal aerial leaves. It is for this reason that the leaves of so many submerged plants, including Water Milfoil (*Myriophyllum spicatum*), Bladderwort (*Utricularia vulgaris*) and Water Violet (*Hottonia palustris*), are finely dissected.

In the following chapters the buttercups of various habitats are described and further aspects of their adaptation are discussed.

Buttercups of meadows and pastures

The best known buttercups are those of meadows and pastures. It is in such open grassy habitats that the three commonest species, Meadow, Creeping and Bulbous Buttercup, occur. These three species are often found growing together and are the three British representatives of section *Ranunculus* of the buttercup genus. The chief characteristics of this section are that the nectaries are covered by a small flap attached at its base and free at the sides, and that the achenes have distinct beaks and are strongly compressed with smooth rather than pitted or spiny sides. When the fruits are ripe the receptacle

Plate 5. *A shallow pond turned white by the massed flowers of a water crowfoot (R. peltatus).*

Plate 6. *Greater Spearwort (R. lingua), the largest British buttercup, growing with reeds and reedmace in a shallow muddy pond.*

Plate 7. *A meadow with buttercups in bloom. The commonest species here is Meadow Buttercup (R. acris) but Bulbous Buttercup is also present in drier patches of ground and Lesser Spearwort (R. flammula) in the wettest places.*

Plate 8. *Lesser Spearwort (R. flammula) is the commonest member of Section Flammula, a group characterised by simple, narrow leaves.*

Plate 9. *Strongly reflexed sepals provide a ready clue to the identity of the Bulbous Buttercup (R. bulbosus).*

Plate 10. *The members of Subgenus Batrachium are easily recognised by their white flowers. This widespread species of water crowfoot (R. peltatus) has palmately lobed floating leaves and finely dissected submerged ones.*

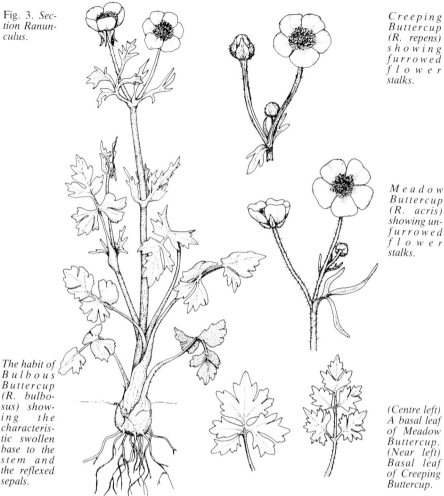

Fig. 3. Section Ranunculus.

Creeping Buttercup (R. repens) showing furrowed flower stalks.

Meadow Buttercup (R. acris) showing unfurrowed flower stalks.

The habit of Bulbous Buttercup (R. bulbosus) showing the characteristic swollen base to the stem and the reflexed sepals.

(Centre left) A basal leaf of Meadow Buttercup. (Near left) Basal leaf of Creeping Buttercup.

elongates by up to three times its original length.

These common species may be distinguished in a variety of ways. Their flowering seasons overlap but are slightly different. The earliest to begin flowering is Bulbous Buttercup, which begins to bloom in April or sometimes even in March. Meadow Buttercup follows towards the end of April or in early May and stays in flower until the beginning of autumn. Creeping Buttercup starts to flower in May and continues in large numbers into August. Thereafter a few flowers may usually be found in sheltered places into November. It is not unusual to find all three in flower together, when they may be distinguished by examining a flower of each.

Bulbous Buttercup may be recognised at once by its strongly reflexed sepals and has its flowers on slightly shorter inflorescences than the other two, which have spreading sepals. Meadow Buttercup has smooth flower stalks whilst those of Creeping Buttercup are furrowed, a difference which can either be seen or felt, by rolling a flower stalk between the fingers.

When flowers are absent the three

Fig. 4. *Sections Echinella and Epirotes.*

Corn Crow-foot (R. arvensis), habit (height 15-60 cm).

Goldilocks (R. auricomus), habit showing flowers with some reduced petals present (height 10-40 cm).

species may be recognised by their leaves. The lower leaves are most useful for this purpose as the upper leaves are all rather similar. The leaves of the Meadow Buttercup are palmately lobed but all the lobes arise directly from the petiole or leaf stalk. In the other two species the central lobe of each leaf has a short stalk separating it from the other lobes and the end of the petiole. In the Creeping Buttercup the stalk of the central leaf lobe is so long that it projects beyond the other lobes; in Bulbous Buttercup it is much shorter and the leaves appear more compact.

Although the three commonest buttercups frequently grow together they do have slightly different geographical ranges and ecological preferences. Bulbous Buttercup prefers slightly drier ground than the other two and in an undulating field will often be found on ridges or hummocks, with Meadow and Creeping Buttercup in the depressions between. Similarly, in a sloping field Bulbous Buttercup is often more abundant in the better drained upper ground than in the lower-lying part of the field. Bulbous Buttercup is less common in the north and west of Britain, which are the areas of highest rainfall. Unlike the other two species, it is not found on mountains.

Creeping Buttercup is common in very damp ground and especially in disturbed places. It can thrive on the heaviest of clay soils and is usually one of the first weeds to colonise such ground after it has been dug over. In common with the Meadow Buttercup, it may be found on the mountains of Snowdonia, the Lake District and Scotland. In such exposed localities the plants are generally smaller in stature, with much shorter inflorescences. Mountain forms of Meadow Buttercup are particularly distinct, usually having much less divided leaves, and some varieties have been given distinct names.

Buttercups belonging to two other sections are also found in open grassy habitats. Section *Ranunculastrum* is represented by a single species, the Fan-leaved Buttercup, which is found in only a few places around St Aubyn in Jersey. It is a rather small plant, reaching only about 30 centimetres (12 inches), with a few somewhat fan-shaped leaves, mostly in a basal rosette. The stems are distinctly hairy and the petals very reflective and glossy.

Three species from section *Echinella* are thought to be native in Britain and one or two others are sometimes found as introduced weeds and have become naturalised. The commonest of the three, Corn Crowfoot, may itself have arrived as an introduced weed in ancient times. The species of this section are annual plants and have achenes with hooks. Corn Crowfoot is most abundant in southern England. Its common name is interesting because it seems that 'crowfoot' is a much older name for *Ranunculus* species than the now universal 'buttercup'. In the printed herbals of the sixteenth and seventeenth centuries the name 'crowfoot' was used almost exclusively, with 'butterflower' and 'buttercup' appearing in works dating from the eighteenth century to the present. Nowadays the name 'crowfoot' is mostly applied to the white-flowered aquatic buttercups but Corn Crowfoot is a reminder that this was not always so.

Hairy Buttercup and Small-flowered Buttercup are much scarcer and more local in distribution. The Hairy Buttercup has reflexed sepals and so could perhaps be confused with the much commoner Bulbous Buttercup, if not in fruit. It can be distinguished by feeling the base of the stems at ground level since it lacks a swollen corm. Small-flowered Buttercup has such small pale petals that it is not easily confused with any other species. Like the former species it has reflexed sepals. It is more a plant of open disturbed ground than of fields and it favours very dry localities.

Woodland buttercups

There are comparatively few kinds of buttercups that penetrate any distance into woods and their numbers diminish the deeper the shade. Of the species of open habitats, Creeping Buttercup is the most tolerant of shade and is often encountered in woods. Even so it is mostly found along woodland margins or in rides and clearings. Where trees have fallen, creating an open space within the wood, species usually found in full light will temporarily move in until ousted by the growth of new shrubs and trees. Only two British species flourish well in woods, Lesser Celandine and Goldilocks.

Lesser Celandine is a very distinctive buttercup. It is instantly recognisable as such but yet is rather different. The petals, which usually number some eleven or twelve, are almost twice as numerous and narrower and more pointed in shape. As the flowers age they gradually lose their yellow colour and become white. Lesser Celandine belongs to a separate subgenus, *Ficaria,* a group of perennial herbs with elongated fleshy root tubers and more or less simple leaves. When ripe the achenes are rounded rather than compressed, although ripe achenes are not always seen as in this species they frequently abort before reaching maturity.

Two very different kinds of celandine occur in Britain and have been recognised as distinct subspecies. It is interesting to search for populations of the two

Plate 11. *From early spring the Lesser Celandine (R. ficaria) may be seen flowering in woods and shady hedgerows. Its rounded, kidney-shaped leaves and narrow petals are very distinctive.*

subspecies as they can often be found quite close together, although they have slightly different habitat preferences. The first, subspecies *ficaria,* is the commoner of the two subspecies and is found in relatively open places, for example along hedgerows and grassy banks. It may even grow in full sunlight and may be recognised by its larger flowers, 2 to 3 centimetres (¾ to 1¼ inches) across, with broad overlapping petals. Subspecies *bulbifer* is usually found in woods and has slightly smaller flowers up to 2 centimetres (¾ inch) across, the petals of which are narrower and do not overlap. The name of this subspecies means 'bulb carrying' and is derived from the fact that it has small rounded bulbils at the bases of the leaf stalks. These can break away and form new plants, a form of purely vegetative reproduction. This is the chief means by which this subspecies reproduces itself, for unlike subspecies *ficaria* its pollen grains are mostly sterile and consequently its flowers set few fertile seeds. The sterility of the pollen is a consequence of the fact that this subspecies is a tetraploid, a plant in which there are twice as many chromosomes as usual in each cell.

Celandines are amongst the earliest flowers to bloom in spring, often flowering with the Wood Anemone (*Anemone nemorosa*). Their fleshy underground tubers store up reserves of food over winter and enable a sudden burst of growth to produce new leaves and then flowers long before many other herbs. A number of woodland species contrive to do this, by means of reserves stored in bulbs or tubers, and in so doing they are able to begin active growth and photosynthesis before the woodland trees come into leaf and reduce the sunlight reaching the woodland floor. One disadvantage of flowering so early is that comparatively few insects are on the wing and opportunities for insect pollination may be restricted. The ability of subspecies *bulbifer* to reproduce itself vegetatively is therefore particularly valuable.

The second woodland buttercup, Goldilocks, flowers later in the year, in April or May, as the woodland trees are coming

17

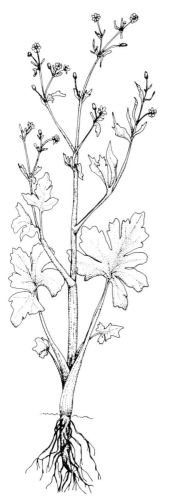

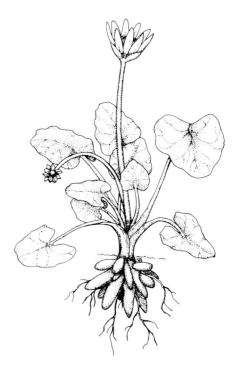

Fig. 5. *Sections Hecatonia and Ficaria (not drawn to scale). (Left) Celery-leaved Crowfoot (R. sceleratus), habit of plant (height 20-60 cm). (Right) Lesser Celandine (R. ficaria), habit of plant (height 5-25 cm).*

into leaf. The most distinctive feature of this species is its peculiar petals, which may resemble those of a typical buttercup or be entirely lacking. Some plants are intermediates, with a few rather lop-sided petals. Goldilocks is another buttercup which reproduces in an unusual way: although pollen grains are necessary for seed to be set they do not fertilise the ovules. The plants are said to be apomictic, because they produce seeds without fertilisation having occurred. Since normal cross-pollination does not occur in Goldilocks the different forms of the plant do not become intermixed but continue as distinct lines.

Yellow-flowered marsh buttercups

Many buttercups thrive in wet places and it is impossible to draw a firm distinction between the species which are essentially plants of open fields and those which inhabit only marshes and water margins.

Fig. 6. Section Flammula (not drawn to scale). (a) Greater Spearwort (R. lingua), habit (height 60-120 cm). (b) Snakestongue Crowfoot (R. ophioglossifolius), habit, showing heart-shaped leaves (height 10-40 cm). (c) Lesser Spearwort (R. flammula), habit (height 10-50 cm). (d) Slender Creeping Spearwort (R. reptans), habit showing arching runners (height 5-25 cm).

Neither is it possible to distinguish between marsh plants and those which may be sometimes fully aquatic. This chapter discusses the yellow-flowered species of wet habitats. The white-flowered aquatics are dealt with in the following chapter.

Two sections of yellow-flowered buttercups grow in habitats dominated by water most of the year round. Section *Hecatonia* is represented by a single species in Britain, the Celery-leaved Crowfoot (*Ranunculus sceleratus*). This is an annual species which sometimes survives over winter and is quite common in suitable habitats in south-eastern Eng-

land, although rare elsewhere. It has thick stems with hollow centres and deeply furrowed surfaces. The leaves are borne on long petioles, which give the plant a celery-like appearance. The lobes of the leaves are much more rounded than those of most other palmate-leaved buttercups.

Section *Flammula* includes four native species and these may be recognised by their distinctive foliage. The leaves are entire, rather than lobed or dissected, and linear to broadly ovate in shape. The leaves often merge in with those of grasses growing with the buttercups. The achenes of this section have long beaks

Plate 12. *Creeping Buttercup (R. repens) can be recognised by its grooved flower stalks as well as by its creeping runners.*

Plate 13. *Meadow Buttercup (R. acris) has cylindrical ungrooved flower stalks which feel smooth when rolled between finger and thumb.*

and are not particularly compressed.

Greater Spearwort is the most handsome member of this section. It is rather local in occurrence but grows in marshes and fens and around the margins of lakes and ponds. Greater Spearwort often grows in amongst other narrow-leaved plants such as Yellow Flag (*Iris pseudacorus*), Reedmace (*Typha latifolia*), Burreed (*Sparganium erectum*) · and Reed (*Phragmites communis*). The similarity of all these species when not in flower sometimes makes it difficult to tell which species are present around a lake where access may be difficult. Greater Spearwort is the tallest British buttercup, often growing to well over 1 metre (3 feet 3 inches). Each autumn it produces a number of rather broad basal leaves from its horizontal stem bases. In the spring the new upright stems begin to grow and the narrower aerial leaves are produced, usually in two ranks on opposite sides of the stems.

Lesser Spearwort (*Ranunculus flammula*) grows to only half the height of the previous species, and often less. It is a widespread and common species, which may be found almost anywhere that is flooded for part of each year. The leaves are of two slightly different kinds, the lower ones being broader and having distinct stalks, the upper ones narrower and without stalks. The flower stalks are often reddish and are furrowed, which those of Greater Spearwort are not. Three distinct subspecies are recognised, two of which are found in coastal and exposed habitats in Scotland and the third being the widespread form, the typical subspecies *flammula*. Subspecies *scotica* is a plant of Scottish loch shores which has unusual narrow strap-like lower leaves which lack the normal expanded blade. Subspecies *minimus* is a dwarf plant which grows to only 15 centimetres (6 inches) at the most and has rather fleshy leaves with cordate, or heart-shaped, bases. This subspecies grows in exposed coastal places in Scotland and the outer isles and also on the western coast of Ireland.

The two remaining members of section *Flammula* are much scarcer plants.

20

Adder's Tongue Crowfoot or Snakestongue Crowfoot (*Ranunculus ophioglossifolius*) is an annual species which now grows only in marshes in Gloucestershire. It was formerly more widespread and occurred in Jersey and Dorset. The drainage of marshes for use as agricultural and building land has reduced the occurrence of many marsh plants, and those which were never common, like the Adder's Tongue Crowfoot, are worst affected. The most distinctive feature of this buttercup are its ovate to cordate lower leaves, which are borne on very long stalks.

The Slender Creeping Buttercup (*Ranunculus reptans*) is another plant which is declining in numbers in Britain. It is found very rarely on lake shores in the Lake District and Scotland and has the unusual growth habit of spreading by means of arching runners which root and produce leaves at each point where they contact the ground. This unusual feature distinguishes the species from Lesser Spearwort, which looks similar. The two species are closely related and it is thought that they can crossbreed to form hybrid plants intermediate between the parent species.

White-flowered aquatic buttercups

At least nine species of white-flowered buttercups occur in Britain. These are the aquatic species known as water crowfoots and belong to subgenus *Batrachium*. Although the petals are predominantly white there is a yellow blotch at the base of each in the British species. The leaves of water crowfoots are stipulate, that is they have small scales known as stipules at each side of the base of the leaf stalk. The achenes of members of this subgenus have distinctive transversely wrinkled sides.

Water crowfoots are difficult plants to identify. One reason for this is that plants of the same species may look very different when found in different localities. Several species have both palmately lobed floating leaves and dissected submerged leaves but the proportion of the two kinds may vary considerably depending, in part, on features of the precise habitat. A few species grow in very shallow water, in places which may well dry out during part of the year, and in such places they may completely lack the dissected leaves. Alternatively, if they are present, then the degree of dissection may be much less and the divided segments themselves may be much shorter and more rigid. The same species growing in deeper water may well have more submerged leaves, with long delicate segments, and fewer floating leaves. The kinds of leaf present in these plants vary with the habitat but in other water crowfoots the leaves are less variable and differences in habitat have no effect. Ivy-leaved Crowfoot (*Ranunculus hederaceus*) and *R. omiophyllus* are two species of muddy places which never have dissected leaves and so are relatively easy to identify. The former species has smaller flowers, only 3 to 6 millimetres (⅛ to ¼ inch) across, than the second, in which they are 8 to 12 millimetres (⅜ to ½ inch).

Four species have both types of leaves and grow in fairly shallow and still water. These are the plants which present most difficulties in identification. The Three-lobed Water Crowfoot (*Ranunculus tripartitus*) does not always have submerged leaves and so can be confused with the two species which always lack them. Its leaves are deeply three-lobed, or sometimes five-lobed, with the lobes all of very similar size. Generally the other species have unequal lobes, but not always. The Common Water Crowfoot (*R. aquatilis*) and *R. baudotii* have transitional leaves intermediate in shape between their dissected and palmate ones. The two species are difficult to distinguish, but *R. baudotii* has a preference for brackish water and so is found in coastal regions. *R. aquatilis* is less tolerant of brackish water and is found far inland in ponds and ditches. The two may be distinguished by the number of achenes present on a fruiting head but this is not an easy character to determine accurately in the field. *R.*

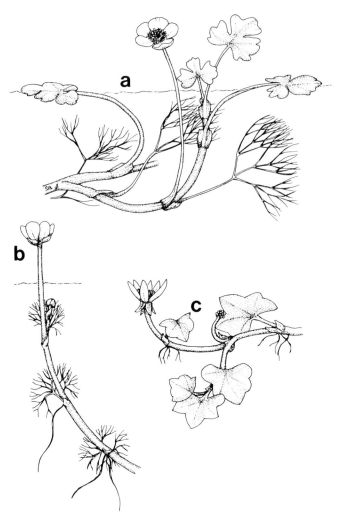

Fig. 7. *Subgenus Batrachium. (a) Water Crowfoot (R. peltatus), a species with both floating and submerged leaves. (b) Water Crowfoot (R. circinatus), a species with submerged leaves only. (c) Ivy-leaved Crowfoot (R. hederaceus), a species which lacks submerged leaves.*

aquatilis rarely has more than forty achenes whereas *R. baudotii* generally has between forty and a hundred. Another very similar species is *R. peltatus*, which is difficult to distinguish from *R. aquatilis*, although it has slightly larger petals and fruit stalks more than 5 centimetres (2 inches) long, whereas those of *R. aquatilis* are usually less than 5 centimetres.

Ranunculus aquatilis lacks floating leaves in one of its many forms, but there are three species which never have them. The crowfoots which have only sub-merged leaves are plants of faster-flowing streams and rivers. *R. fluitans* can grow in strong currents, anchored to the bottom by creeping runners from which the trailing stems may extend as much as 6 metres (20 feet) in length. The individual leaves are usually 8 to 30 centimetres (3 to 12 inches) in length, greenish black, and they consist of narrow filamentous strands divided two or three times along their length. *R. circinatus* has submerged leaves whose repeatedly divided filamentous segments are quite short and all lie in one plane with a circular outline.

It grows in slow streams, ditches and ponds and its leaves are fairly rigid so that they will maintain their circular, flattened shape when the plant is lifted out of the water.

Ranunculus trichophyllus has leaves divided repeatedly into threes and the segments do not all lie in one plane. The tips of each segment are a darker green and the leaves are soft and delicate so that they do not maintain their shape when lifted from the water but collapse and hang limply.

Identifying such variable plants as the water crowfoots is made more complex by the fact that several of the species form hybrids intermediate in appearance between their parents. When in flower, the water crowfoots are a distinctive and spectacular sight. There are, however, a few plants which may be mistaken for water crowfoots. One is the unrelated Lesser Water Plantain (*Baldellia ranunculoides*), which has leaves rather like those of the Lesser Spearwort and flowers very similar to those of a water crowfoot. Even the heads of fruits resemble buttercup achenes. Lesser Water Plantain is a monocotyledonous plant unrelated to the buttercups and has its flower parts arranged in groups of three. The presence of three white petals is the easiest way of recognising the plant. Water Violet (*Hottonia palustris*) has divided submerged leaves and flowers with white petals, each with a yellow blotch at the base. It can easily be distinguished from a water crowfoot by the fact that its flowers are not solitary but in whorls around a long inflorescence.

The folklore of buttercups

Many familiar wild flowers have interesting traditional associations related to their properties and uses in times past. Such associations are often reflected in the various common names which have been used through the centuries, sometimes staying in use long after the reasons for their origin have become obscure.

Buttercups have been known by many names, some applicable to any member of the genus *Ranunculus* and to some closely related plants, others much more specific.

Some of the common names of buttercups simply refer to the colour as, for example, Gold Cup, Goldweed, Gilted Cup, Yellow Cup and Yellow Creams. The cup names refer to the shape of the newly opened flowers and include Kingcup. This name is used equally for buttercups and their larger-flowered relative Marsh Marigold (*Caltha palustris*) and demonstrates the way in which common names may link together plants which, although related, are placed in different groups by botanists because of important but less obvious differences.

The bright yellow petals of buttercups, plants which often grow where cows graze, have long been associated with butter, even though the name 'buttercup' has a shorter pedigree than 'crowfoot'. Other 'butter' names include Butter Daisy, Butterchurn, Butter Rose and Butter Flowers. From the butter coloured flowers grew the superstition that buttercups could improve the quality of milk given by cows and in the past the flowers were sometimes rubbed on the teats of cows to improve their yield. When children use buttercups 'to see if you like butter' they continue this traditional association.

Lesser Celandine in particular was especially associated with butter, for it has long root tubers reminiscent of a cow's udder. Groups of four tubers were sometimes hung in the cowshed or dairy to symbolise udders and were thought to encourage creamy milk. Lesser Celandine is one of the most distinctive species of buttercup and has several common names of its own, including Spring Messenger, which refers to its early flowering season, Golden Stars and Starflower, which reflect the narrow-petalled, star-shaped flowers. Yet another name for the species was Pilewort, which referred to the use of extracts made from the roots in the treatment of piles.

Extracts of the roots of other buttercups were used as medicines for different ailments. Lesser Spearwort, Meadow and Bulbous Buttercups in particular were used to produce blisters on the skin, which were thought to be beneficial in curing diseases by drawing out the poisons which caused them. The blisters were caused by the irritant effect of a toxic substance called anemonin, which is a yellow volatile oil present in all buttercups but more abundant in some species than others. It is ironic that this substance can cause a reduction in the milk yielded by cows which have eaten buttercups in quantity. Furthermore the milk may become tainted with a bitter taste. Fortunately buttercup plants themselves taste distinctly bitter and are almost invariably avoided by livestock. Serious poisoning is therefore a very rare occurrence but one species, Celery-leaved Buttercup, may cause problems because it has particularly succulent and attractive foliage and is often eaten when better grazing is scarce. The names Blister Plant and Blister Cup recall the medicinal usage of the blistering properties of buttercups. One method of applying the medicine, which was prepared by pounding the roots, was to fill empty shells of limpets and apply these to the areas to be treated. This medicine was used as a treatment for bubonic plague during the time of the great plague in Europe, when desperate remedies were used even if they proved unsuccessful.

The Corn Crowfoot has names derived both from the nuisance it caused as a weed of corn fields and from its large and unusual achenes. Hellweed, Hungerweed and Jackweed are names which emphasise the harm caused by the plant as a weed, whilst Cog Wheels, Crow Claws and Scratch Bur are descriptive of the achenes and Cogweed refers to both characteristics of the plant.

The white-flowered buttercups have fewer names and no distinction is made in them between the different species. This is surprising for, although individually the plants are small and inconspicuous, they frequently bloom in such masses that they completely transform a pond or stream, turning it pure white for several weeks during the height of the flowering season. Besides the name water crowfoot, the plants are sometimes called Water Lily or Water Anemone.

BIBLIOGRAPHY

Clapham, A. R., Tutin, T. G., and Warburg, E. F. *Flora of the British Isles.* Cambridge University Press, 1962.

Fitter, R. S. R. *Finding Wild Flowers.* Collins, 1981.

Fitter, R. S. R., Fitter A., and Blamey, M. *Wild Flowers of Britain and Northern Europe.* Collins, 1980.

Gilmour, J., and Walters, M. *Wild Flowers.* Collins New Naturalist Series, Collins, 1969.

Grigson, G. *The Englishman's Flora.* Paladin, 1975.

Keeble-Martin, W. *The Concise British Flora in Colour.* Ebury Press, 1965.

Press, J. R., Sutton, D. A., and Tebbs, B. M. *Field Guide to the Flowers of Britain.* Readers Digest, 1981.

ACKNOWLEDGEMENTS

Photographs are acknowledged as follows: P. Lund, plate 1; D. A. Sutton, plate 5. All other photographs and illustrations, including the cover picture, are by the author.